How to Sp...
Disco Diva

An essential **Bubblegum** guide

Ged Backland and Phil Renshaw

Disco Diva

When you get glammed up for groovin'
you feel that funky fever
You're delicious and delightful
you're a diamond Disco Diva!

Disco Diva

'Gorgeously glitteringly glam' is the only way you can describe Disco Diva. She's a twenty-four hour party girl with an ear for a big boomin' seventies' anthem. She loves to dance around at home and to the stereo in Boy Racer's car. She'll jump in, turn the volume up on his stereo and declare "Disco Diva's in the house". She's a one-way ticket to the 'in-crowd' and people tend to worship the ground she dances on. Slightly dippy, but who cares when you're this gorgeous?

Most Likely to Say... Turn it up!

Most Likely to Be... On the dance floor

Fave Colour Candy Pink

Bestest Friends with... Nutty Tart

Dancing Queen

Boy Racer

Boom Boom Boom Boom

SPEED1

Late at night when most of the crew
are fast asleep in their houses
Disco Diva's freaking out
flapping her disco trousers.

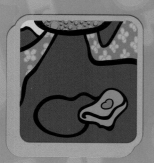

Disco Diva's in her own world
when people shout, she just shrugs
She can't hear 'cos she has headphones
stuck in her flippin' lugs.

Toot
Toot

Boy Racer loves to race about
cruising for an admiring glance
Disco Diva just catches a lift
then slaps on some Kickin' Dance.

Club Bubba

Some nights are saved for staying in
and soaking in the tub
But not for Disco Diva
she just loves to club!

Gym Queen spends all her cash
on the latest fitness craze
Disco Diva spends hers on sounds
and boogies for bloomin' days!

Diamond Geezer always dances
with funky Disco Diva
And every night is Saturday night
when you've got that disco fever!

Happenin' Babe gets loads of looks
she lives life in a whirl
But even she can't keep up
with this crazy dancing girl!

Blonde Bombshell is a hip lass
all big hair and red lip gloss
But she knows at movin' and groovin'
Disco Diva is the boss!

Designer Diva wears the latest threads
to make her look all chic
Disco Diva chucks on clubbin' clothes
and wears them the whole week!

Curry Monster loves things really hot
he eats curries by the score
But even he can't bear the heat
of five hours on the floor!

Drama Queen likes to make
a scene out of every song
Disco Diva gets on one groove
and it lasts her all night long.

Shoe Queen tries to totter along
on her way into the town
But when she dances with Disco Diva
she ends up tumbling down!

Slap Head likes to strut his stuff
he never wants to go home
He dances madly with Disco Diva
as lights bounce off his dome!

So there you have it, it's all very clear
The low-down on the Diva's here.

If it all sounds familiar, if it rings true
Chances are, the Diva's you!